This book belongs to

....

Illustrated by Dawn Machell
Written by Hayley Down.

THE STORY OF
CHRISTMAS

Dawn Machell • Hayley Down

make
believe
ideas

THE ANGEL'S NEWS

An **angel** flew on **golden** wings
to tell Mary **surprising** things:
"My dear, you are God's **chosen** one –
and you are **pregnant** with His Son."

MARY AND ELIZABETH

Mary's cousin was **pregnant** too.
When they **met**, Elizabeth knew
Mary was **blessed** by God above,
for her **Son** would **bring** the world such love.

JOURNEY TO BETHLEHEM

A new law meant Joseph must go

on a trip that was long and slow.

He took Mary to Bethlehem,

with a little donkey helping them.

FINDING THE STABLE

In Bethlehem no rooms were free
for Joseph and his family.
At last, they found a place to stay:
a warm, dry stable filled with hay.

JESUS IS BORN!

Jesus was born that very night
under a **star** that shone so **bright**.
When it was time to **rest** His head,
they used a **manger** for His bed.

THE ANGELS' MESSAGE

Outside, some **shepherds** watched their sheep —
careful not to fall **asleep**.
A group of **angels** came to say,
"The Son of God is **born** today!"

THE SHEPHERDS' VISIT

The shepherds rushed to see the boy

who was to bring the world such joy.

They left and then told everyone

that they had met God's only Son.

FOLLOWING THE STAR

Riding camels in lands afar,
wise men saw the shining star.
They went along a dusty road
with special gifts inside their load.

GIVING GIFTS

They met the boy and bowed their heads.

Overjoyed, the wise men said,

"This is God's Son, as was foretold!

Please take this frankincense, myrhh, and gold."

JESUS HAS RISEN!

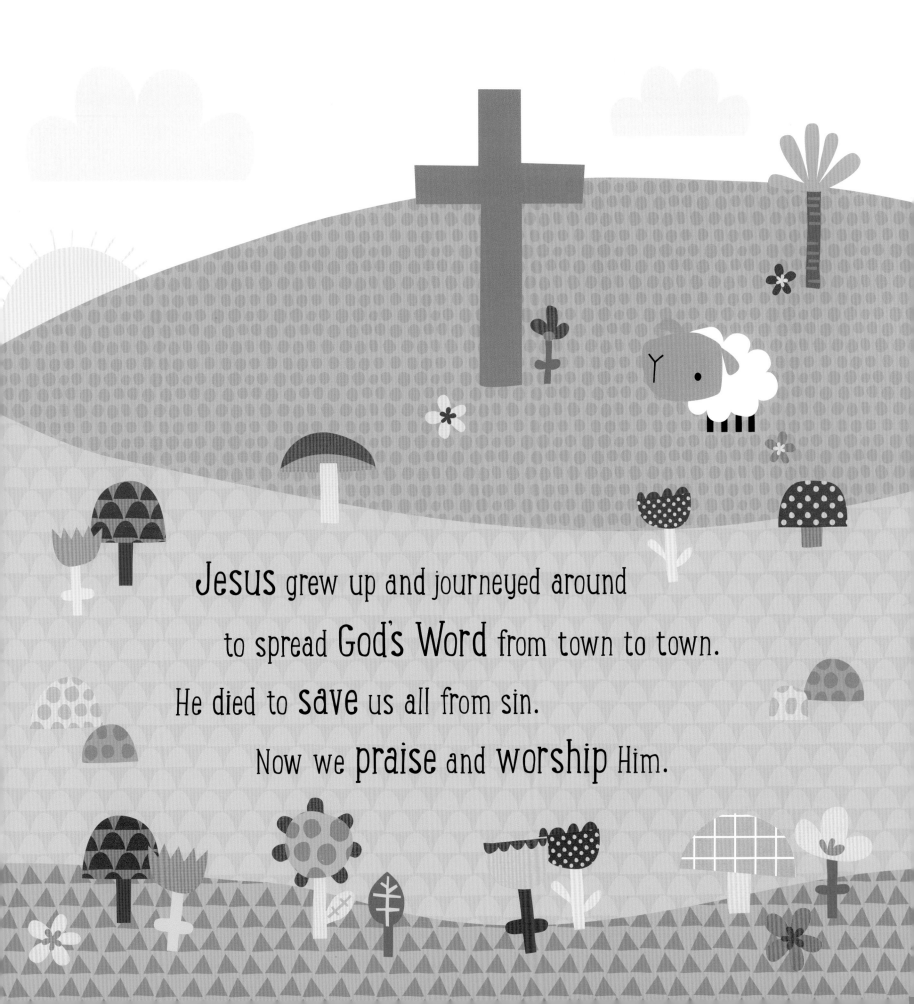

Jesus grew up and journeyed around
to spread God's Word from town to town.

He died to save us all from sin.

Now we praise and worship Him.

The End